WHITE ISLA

New Zealand's Most Active Vol

PETER AND JENNY TAIT

To our son Isaac

A GODWIT BOOK
published by
Random House New Zealand
18 Poland Road, Glenfield, Auckland, New Zealand
www.randomhouse.co.nz

First published 2001

ISBN 1 86962 090 9

Cover and text design: Dexter Fry
Layout: Sharon Grace, Grace Design
Front cover photograph: Brian Enting, BLUESTREAM LTD
Map artwork pages 4 and 19 : Jonette Surridge
Printed in Singapore

CONTENTS

WHITE ISLAND

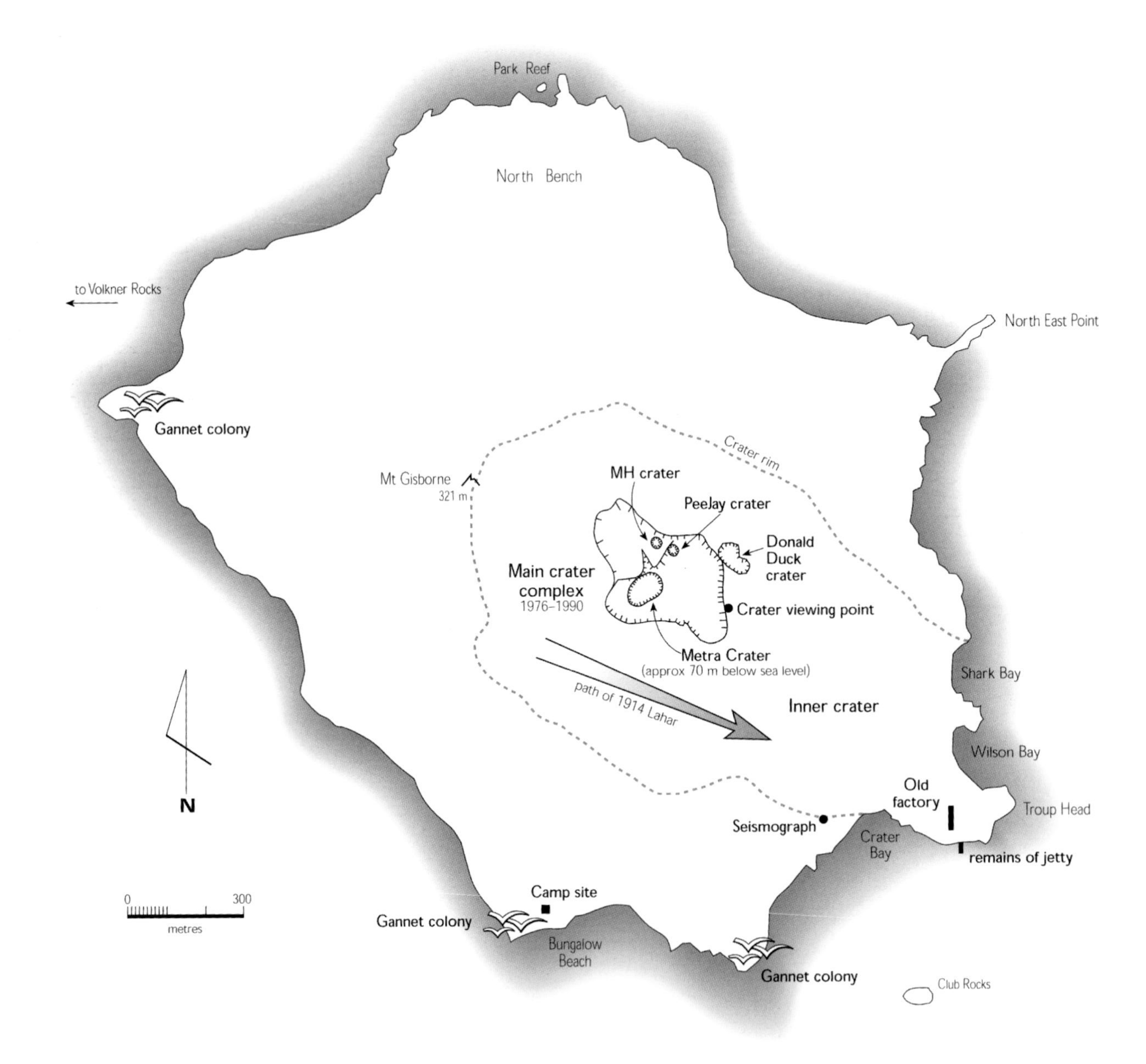

Above: *Buildings on White Island immediately before the 1914 disaster.* (Tauranga Museum)

Inset: *A close-up of the buildings on White Island just before the 1914 disaster.* (Joan Earwaker and Beverley Millar)

INTRODUCTION

White Island is the summit of a large submarine volcano believed to be 150,000 – 200,000 years old. It is New Zealand's most active volcano and lies 49 km north of Whakatane in the Bay of Plenty.

Although the volcano reaches 321 metres above sea level, its full height from the sea floor is about 760 metres. Of its 16 km by 18 km breadth all that is visible above the sea is the island measuring 2.4 km by 2 km. The sea stacks of Club Rocks and Volkner Rocks are visible to the south and west of the volcano.

Small it might be, but White Island has a grim past. In September 1914 the western rim of the volcano's crater collapsed, unleashing a volcanic landslide, or lahar, which killed 10 men who were working on the island as sulphur miners. Mining resumed some years later but eventually ceased in 1933, leaving the island to nature.

ABOVE: *Rescuers digging for survivors, September 1914. Sergeant James Ferguson* of the Opotiki Police led the rescue party.*
(Joan Earwaker and Beverley Millar)

* *(centre, with hand on hip)*

Since 1967 scientists have closely monitored activity on the island, which regularly releases plumes of ash and steam into the air, visible from the mainland. Today it is possible to visit White Island as a tourist and witness its remarkable features at first hand.

The island's lunar landscape and constant volcanic activity make it one of the most awesome scenic attractions in the country. The bright yellow sulphurous vents, the smell of the volcanic gases and rumbling of the inner earth under your feet provide a unique experience.

Vegetation exists on the outer walls of the island but is sparse, testament to the effects of the volcanic activity. Grey-faced petrels nest in great numbers in the soft ash of the outer crater and Australasian gannets establish fascinating colonies in the summer among the ice-plant, with the blue haze of ammonia chloride forming a cloud above.

Snorkelling or diving around White Island is spectacular, with underwater volcanic vents, soft corals, colourful sponges and an abundance of fish life.

And amidst it all are the remains of the buildings built by the early sulphur mining companies, now abandoned to time and the elements.

A VOLCANO DISCOVERED

THE FIRST EUROPEAN to discover White Island was Captain James Cook (then Lieutenant) on 31 October 1769: 'At 8 saw land which made like an island bearing west.'

Then on 1 November 1769: 'The land seen yesterday bearing west and which we now saw was an island bore SW [this should be NW] distant 8 leagues. I have named it White Island because as such it always appear'd to us.'

It wasn't until 1 December 1826, when the Reverend Henry Williams, a naval officer turned missionary, sailed to White Island aboard the 60-ton schooner *Herald*, that anyone realised it was a volcano. Williams stated 'the

ABOVE: *The original works built at Crater Bay, 1923. These were much improved in later years.*
(Whakatane Museum)

INSET: *Loading 'White Island Product' onto the* Paroto. *The rock mined on White Island was rich in sulphur.*
(Whakatane Museum)

ABOVE: *Railway lines were constructed to run tramway dumptrucks from the quarry to the factory.* (Whakatane Museum)

INSET: *Fordson tractor towing the steam engine. The working life of tractors and trucks on the island was very short, because of the corrosive nature of the acidic atmosphere.* (Whakatane Museum)

whole island was composed of sulphur'.

The first map of White Island was made in 1866 by government surveyor Edwin Davy. While ownership of the island was claimed by local Maori, the government decided otherwise and deemed it Crown land.

Bay of Plenty trader Philip Tapsell purchased the island in the late 1830s for two hogsheads (barrels) of rum and then in 1868 it passed to his son Retireti and daughter Kataraina. The following year ownership was transferred to Kataraina's husband George Simpkins, who sold it in 1874 to John Wilson and William Kelly. Kelly sold his half share in 1876 to John Mowbray, who almost immediately sold it to Frank Troup.

LEFT: *Bagging the product from the three 80-ton concrete hoppers. White Island Product was marketed as fertiliser that contained approximately 40% sulphur.* (Whakatane Museum)

ABOVE: *The remains of a truck and trailer, 1936. Model T Ford trucks and trailers were used to transport rock from areas of the island not serviced by railway lines.* (J. Dent)

Henry Johnson bought Troup's half share in 1885 and together with Wilson started the first sulphur mine. This operation didn't last long, ceasing in 1886 after the Tarawera eruption. Some obviously believed White Island offered a similar threat.

Henry Johnson sold some of his share to the Bank of New Zealand and George Morris, and this new group resumed mining in 1898. This ran for three years before it collapsed in 1901. Andrew Gray acquired the island in 1907 but made no attempts to mine and in 1913 sold it to Archibald Mercer and John Browne, who were acting on behalf of the White Island Sulphur Company Ltd, of Vancouver.

Mining commenced again in February 1914 but it wasn't long before disaster struck. After only three months of operation one of the large retorts used in extracting the sulphur suddenly burst. A fireman called John Williams was severely burned and died later that evening. The plant was closed for repairs, but this was not the last tragedy to occur that year.

Shortly after Williams' death Donald Pye, another fireman, went missing. The only trace of him ever found was his boots. It was thought he had committed suicide by jumping into a crater, although when you visit

ABOVE: *Looking from Crater Bay at the derelict factory, 1978. Note the remains of the three large hoppers in front of the building.* (A. Moore)

INSET: *The remains of a lifeboat, 1936, which was used for travelling between camp and Crater Bay, and also for fishing trips.* (J. Dent)

White Island today you realise it would be an easy place to dispose of an unwanted body . . .

In September 1914 the south-western rim of the crater collapsed, causing a lahar to sweep down the crater floor, bulldozing the boilerhouse, retort house, the cookhouse/dining room, the manager's quarters and the men's accommodation out to sea.

Ten lives were lost in this disaster. The only survivor was the local cat, named Peter, and renamed Peter the Great. Rescue parties dug trenches through the steaming debris but no trace was ever found of men or buildings. Some wreckage from the living quarters and lifeboats was washed up on the shore between Maketu and Tauranga soon after.

Naturally enough, mining attempts on White Island were abandoned, but only until 1923. At this point Archibald Mercer acquired title to the island in his own name and set about raising money to have another go at mining the sulphur. He established White Island Agriculture Chemical Company Ltd, which was registered in Vancouver and raised capital by selling shares. (In later years this company became White Island Products, based in New Zealand.) The sharebroking firm G.A. Buttle & Company was enlisted to sell shares in New Zealand and a prospectus grossly exaggerated the 'immense' quantities of minerals awaiting extraction.

ABOVE: *The derelict factory, 1970, showing remnants of the 60 ft rotary drier.* (A. Moore)

By 1925 a new factory had been constructed close to Crater Bay, on the debris from the 1914 lahar. But this time the men's living quarters were constructed on the southern benches of the island in an area known today as Bungalow Beach.

Mining continued into the 1930s, but with the Depression and the consequent reduced demand for fertiliser, the company was never able to return a profit and all efforts ceased in 1933.

White Island was put up for tender and was eventually bought by George Raymond Buttle in June 1936. When the new owner was asked why he wanted to own White Island he said he 'rather liked the idea of owning a volcano' and, 'Strange as it may seem, the island is unbelievably beautiful and beyond description. Surely it is one of the wonders of the world'.

In 1953 Buttle was approached by the Commissioner of Crown Lands seeking to buy the island on behalf of the government. He was unwilling to sell but a compromise was reached and in December 1953, White Island became a private scenic reserve.

Ownership passed to Buttle's son John in 1957 and then to the Gwen Buckland Buttle No. 2 Trust in 1996.

ABOVE: *The miners' living quarters at Bungalow Beach, 1929.* (C. Bryenton)

INSET: *Landing back at camp after fishing. All boats had to be lifted and taken from high water.* (C. Bryenton)

A MINER'S LIFE

RALPH BRYENTON lived and worked on White Island for almost two years and he reckoned life there was not too bad.

Ralph had finished his apprenticeship as a mechanic in 1929 and heard there was work going on White Island through a company in Tauranga. It was the Depression and jobs were scarce so there was never any lack of applicants. In fact jobs did not need to be advertised: men would walk the length of the country in search of work.

But for some who signed on with White Island Products, the sight from the ship of the island belching away and its formidable terrain was too much.

ABOVE: *The factory in 1930, viewed from the crater rim. The factory was built on material deposited by the lahar in 1914.* (C. Bryenton)

INSET: *Very little remains of the miners' living quarters at Bungalow Beach. Tour guides Jo and Kirsten pose with the remnants of a chimney. Note the lack of vegetation.*

When the ship anchored they stayed aboard and travelled straight back home. Ralph recalled one man who climbed the mast, tied himself to it and refused to come down until the ship had started its return journey.

Ralph chose to stay, and put his mechanical skills to good use in keeping the machinery running. He lived at the campsite at Bungalow Beach, where each man had a hut of his own. Bungalow Beach is on the outer crater wall on the southern side of the island. After the landslide of 1914, it was decided no one should live in the inner crater area again. By all accounts it was a pleasant campsite, with views out to sea and surrounded by a pohutukawa forest, with gannets nesting near by.

There was little to do out of working hours. The men played a lot of cards, had a go at making home brew, went fishing and made carvings from pohutukawa wood. But Ralph said life was good. 'You couldn't afford to buy a beer in town anyway!'

The main problem was getting to work. On calm days they lowered small

ABOVE: *The supply ship* Paroto, *washed ashore on White Island in 1929.* (C. Bryenton)

RIGHT: *Ralph with the mask used to frighten visitors.* (C. Bryenton)

RIGHT (INSET): *Coming ashore on Bungalow Beach.* (C. Bryenton)

boats into the water and made their way around to Crater Bay. However, when the sea was rough the men had to walk the dreaded track along the outer crater wall. This path was narrow and precipitous, gradually weaving its way up and around the southern wall until it reached the rim overlooking Crater Bay, then zigzagging steeply down to the crater floor.

Supply ships were scheduled to bring food and water each week but in the winter months, when the winds blew largely from the south, the vessels would often be delayed. Sometimes it was up to three weeks before fresh supplies could be delivered. During these periods the men lived predominantly on fish and rice, which took its toll. Back on the mainland Ralph was recorded as saying, 'After having lived on the island on these rations, I have since never eaten another grain of rice'.

On one occasion the supply ship, *Paroto*, lost its anchorage and was washed ashore. It took several days before another ship from Auckland reached the island and was able to tow it off and make sufficient repairs to sail it back to Tauranga.

Ralph was aware of the latent power of the ground they were living on but it did not particularly bother him. He recalled that when a film crew visited the island to make a story about the 1914 disaster they left behind a dummy they used in the filming. The miners had endless fun terrifying visiting tourists by leaving it lying on the beach!

Ralph celebrated his 21st birthday on White Island in September 1930. A friend, Meg Abbott, later told him how she and some friends had lit a bonfire on Waiotahi Beach that night, optimistic that he would see it and know they were celebrating for him.

Ralph left White Island in 1931. When he died in 1996 his ashes were returned to the island, where no doubt he watches over each visiting boatload.

ABOVE: *Chemists from the Institute of Geological and Nuclear Sciences collecting samples from one of the many fumeroles on White Island.* (C.P. Wood, IGNS)

MONITORING THE VOLCANO

WHITE ISLAND is the northernmost volcano in the Taupo Volcanic Zone, which contains most of New Zealand's active volcanoes. The Taupo Volcanic Zone is a 20–40 km-wide band that extends 240 km north-east from Mt Ruapehu. It was formed along the line where the Pacific Plate meets the Indian-Australian Plate.

Although ash eruptions and volcanic activity have been reported on White Island since the 1830s it was not until 1967 that a scientific monitoring programme was set up. Scientists from the Department of Scientific and Industrial Research (DSIR) and Victoria University in Wellington began the work, which is now run by the Institute of Geological and Nuclear Sciences (IGNS) based in the Research Centre at Wairakei.

The most obvious piece of scientific equipment on White Island is the seismograph, installed in 1976. Visitors can see its solar panels when standing on the crater floor, looking up to the southern rim of the crater. Monitored 24 hours a day, the seismograph measures earthquakes and volcanic tremors. The information is recorded at IGNS's Wairakei base, then sent on to Wellington. During active periods the solar panels are often coated with ash and the seismic equipment itself bombarded with rock, making recording difficult.

Scientists are not based on the island but make five or six visits a year. One of the things they do is record ground deformation. Survey pegs can be seen at strategic locations. These help measure swelling or deflation of the crater floor, giving an indication of possible lifting or retraction of magma. The pegs often become buried during eruptions and need to be replaced.

LEFT: *Solar panels for the seismograph coated in ash. Monitoring equipment suffers terribly during eruptive periods.* (B.J. Scott, IGNS)

ABOVE: *A bathymetric rendering around White island shows the massive volcanic structure which is below sea level.*

RIGHT: *The intersecting line of the Indian-Australian Plate and the Pacific Plate bisects New Zealand (inset, left). The Taupo volcanic zone is a narrow belt of volcanic activity extending north-east from below Mt Ruapehu up to and beyond White Island.*

Visiting scientists also collect samples from the island's streams and fumeroles, from which they can study the volcano's gas and water chemistry. The results supply another clue to the puzzle of what is happening beneath the surface.

It is thought that over 90 submarine volcanoes occur along the Tonga-Kemadec volcanic arc running north-east of White Island. In 1999 the New Zealand American Plume Mapping Expedition (NZAPLUME) research cruise ship surveyed 13 submarine volcanoes along the southern part of the arc to the north of White Island. Seven submarine volcanoes were discovered to have active hydrothermal vent ('black smoker') fields (*See map, opposite*). Hydrothermal vents were also discovered offshore from White Island, some of which contained liquid mercury!

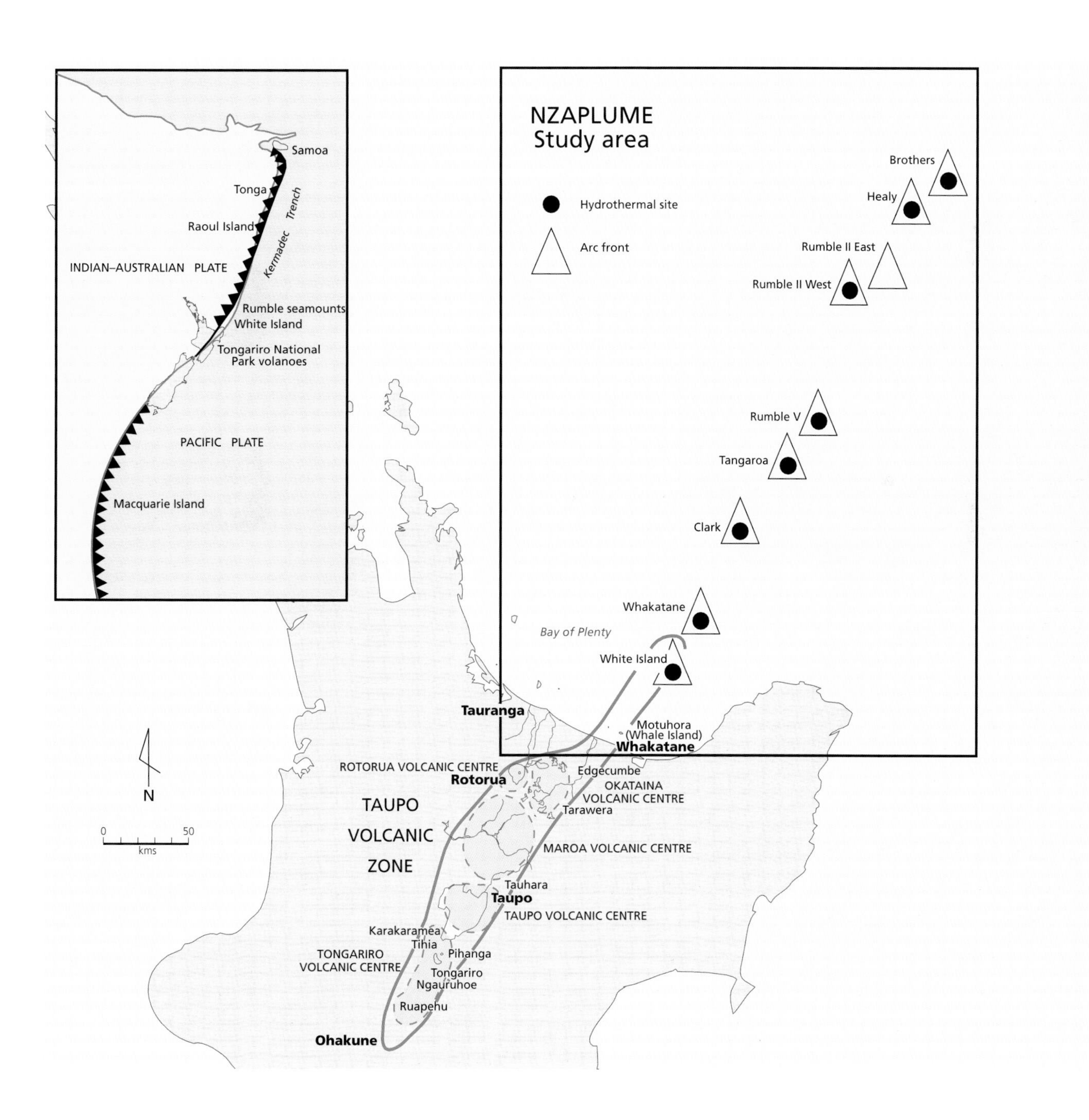
Samoa
Tonga
Kermadec Trench
Raoul Island
INDIAN–AUSTRALIAN PLATE
Rumble seamounts
White Island
Tongariro National Park volanoes
PACIFIC PLATE
Macquarie Island
NZAPLUME Study area
Hydrothermal site
Arc front
Brothers
Healy
Rumble II East
Rumble II West
Rumble V
Tangaroa
Clark
Whakatane
Bay of Plenty
White Island
Tauranga
Motuhora (Whale Island)
Whakatane
ROTORUA VOLCANIC CENTRE
Rotorua
Edgecumbe
OKATAINA VOLCANIC CENTRE
Tarawera
TAUPO VOLCANIC ZONE
MAROA VOLCANIC CENTRE
Tauhara
Taupo
TAUPO VOLCANIC CENTRE
Karakaraméa
Tihia
Pihanga
TONGARIRO VOLCANIC CENTRE
Tongariro
Ngauruhoe
Ruapehu
Ohakune
N
0
50
kms

Above: *Monitoring the deformation of the surface. By mapping the height changes taken from a network of survey pegs, the scientists gain information on the events occurring below. The surface inflates and deflates, a bit like a balloon, during injection or retraction of magma.*
(B.J. Scott, IGNS)

With increased tourism to White Island any changes on the surface of the island are regularly reported back to the scientists by guides. Residents of the Bay of Plenty also keep an eye on their icon and often phone in with reports if they think the island has erupted. If there is no wind the island's regular steam emission can billow thousands of feet into the air, forming a large mushroom cloud. This is a handy weather vane for local boaties!

Of course no amount of scientific monitoring can guarantee that there will be any warning of an eruption, and as tour guides we acknowledge this risk. But in all the years that tourists have been visiting, no one has been seriously injured by volcanic activity.

When we're asked whether we feel safe guiding on a live volcano we reply that we feel safer on White Island than driving a car on the road!

ERUPTION! 27 JULY 2000

YOU CAN READ ALL THE BOOKS on volcanoes, you can scan the pictures and study the diagrams, but it's not until you witness the events and changes of a volcano first hand that you can truly appreciate the power of this earth we live on.

Early in March 2000, three small vents developed on the northern wall of the main crater complex. The pressure in these vents slowly built up until on 7 March one of them started to emit ash. As this continued the three vents slowly merged into one and kept growing. This vent was then named the MH crater (scientists need to name craters for recording purposes).

On 19 April the Scientific Alert Level was raised from 1 to 2, meaning the likelihood of rocks and tephra being ejected had increased.

BELOW: *In New Zealand two methods exist for measuring the alert status of volcanoes. One is for 'Reawakening Volcanoes' and the other is used in managing 'Frequently Active Volcanoes', like White Island. Scientists at the Institute of Geological and Nuclear Sciences monitor White Island and assign alert levels ranging from 0 to 5.*

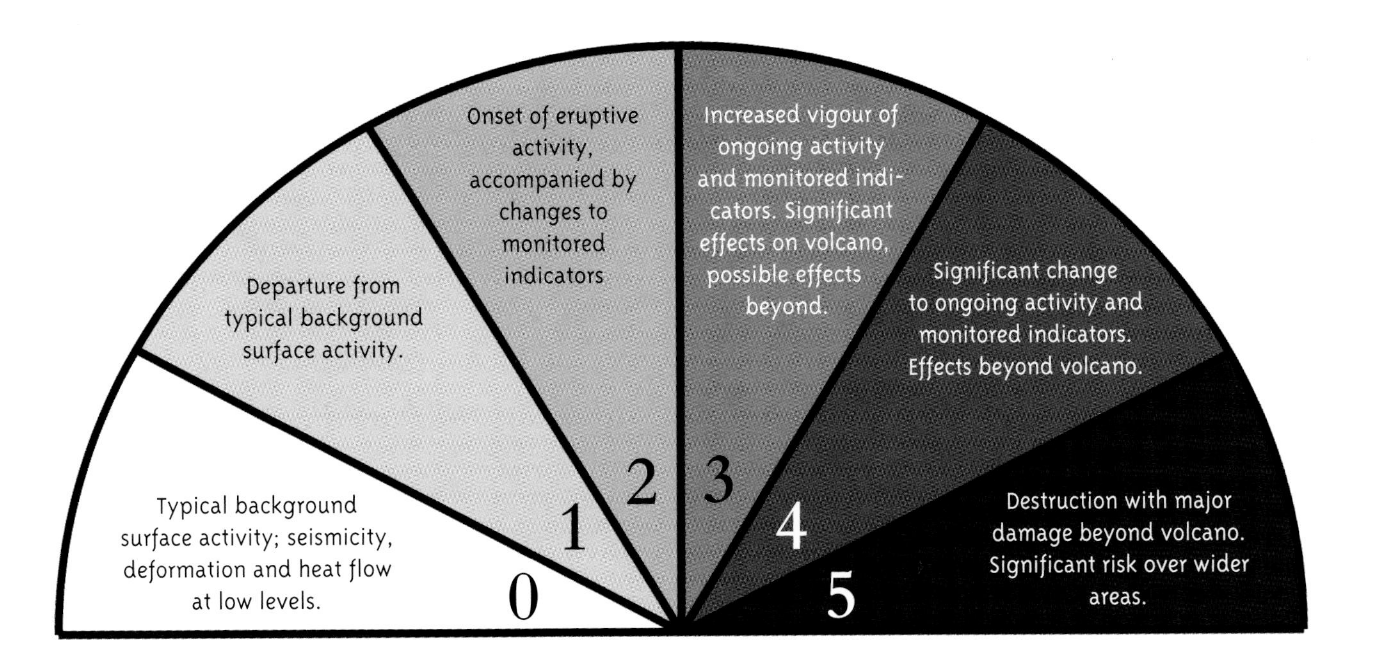

ABOVE: *Where is all this ash coming from? 1976–1990 crater complex, 1 July.*

ABOVE RIGHT: *Lake nearly reaching vent edge, 25 July.*

For about three weeks the ash emitted was wet, making the ground slippery. The lack of traction restricted visitor access but did not last long.

Over this period many new layers of ash were added, so that it was like walking in powder snow, with no footsteps to follow. In the wrong wind conditions, however, visitors left the island coated in the 'fallout'.

The question was, where was all this material coming from? Surely a huge cavity must have been developing somewhere below the surface. Eventually in July we got our answer. We visited the island right up until 25 July, when it was 'ashing' as usual. On 26 July staff from the Institute of Geological and Nuclear Sciences visited and issued the following public statement:

Past activity at White Island indicates that explosive eruptions, some ejecting large rocks over the island, could occur with little or no warning under the current conditions. Such eruptions would pose a significant hazard to anyone on the island at the time. If material collapses into the conduit then a strong gas flow may erupt that material explosively and throw it some distance from the vent. During such activity the risk to anyone on the island will be greater than that during the last three months. Caution should be exercised at all times. Alert level remains at 2.

LEFT: *Where's the lake? 29 July.*

ABOVE: *Is this Mars? Now the western half of the island is coated in red ash, 30 July.*

Bad weather prevented tours to White Island until 29 July, when we found a totally altered landscape. Stepping ashore onto the wharf (at least 700 metres from the source of the activity) we sank into mud and scoria a good 200 mm thick. We ploughed our way through the debris up to the main crater area to find the lake had been displaced and a new explosion crater of 120–150 metres across had formed.

Back at the boat we notified the scientists of our findings and after checking the seismograph it was agreed that the eruption had probably occurred on 27 July, around 6 pm. No residents from the mainland had reported any unusual emissions from the island on this day, probably due to lack of light at this time in the middle of winter. However, we later found out that residents of Te Kaha had heard strange rumblings on the evening of 27 July.

By the next day there had been another change: red ash had turned most of the island a dark rusty red.

Continual 'ashing' occurred until the beginning of September, when the alert level was lowered back to 1.

During this active period, although we continued to run tours, we had to be extremely vigilant, ensuring that our customers knew the risks and that we had competent staff on the island at all times. Cleaning duty (gas masks, helmets, clothing and the boat) was never ending, but the privilege of being able to witness this expression of the earth's power made it more than worthwhile.

ABOVE: *Visitors can venture right up to the rim of the crater when conditions are favourable.*

FAR LEFT: *Formed in April 1999, the PeeJay crater was named after Peter and Jenny Tait. Following the eruption of July 2000, as the MH crater grew, PeeJay ceased to emit steam and gas and the crater died. It is now a barely visible hole covered with ash.*

ABOVE: *Sulphur deposits can grow to form high columns. These eventually collapse due to their sheer weight, with heavy rainfall or from movement caused by volcanic tremors.*

ABOVE RIGHT: *Bright yellow sulphur crystals form as volcanic gases cool.*

BELOW RIGHT: *Long dry periods allow gases seeping through the island's surface to crystallise and form a wonderful garden-like display. Unfortunately rain will wash this spectacle away.*

THE SEARCH FOR SULPHUR

WHY DID SO MANY PEOPLE invest so much money in sulphur? Why did men agree to work and live on a volcano, some ultimately sacrificing their lives?

Gross exaggerations about the quantity and quality of the sulphur on White Island led to several attempts to harvest the 'product'. The New Zealand Manure and Chemical Company was the first on the scene, set up in 1885 to produce fertiliser for the local market and sulphur ore for export. Though their efforts were doomed their initial excitement was understandable when you peruse the publicity of the time:

- 'White Island contains the only deposit of high-grade sulphur of any magnitude in the Empire.'
- 'The deposits of sulphur in the crater at White Island are vast.'
- 'Sulphur in pure form exists at the westerly end of the crater in great quantities. These deposits, however, fade to insignificance when one begins to investigate the numerous deposits of high-grade sulphur ore, which runs from 50% to 85% and 90% pure sulphur.'
- 'The deposits of material on the island suitable for crushing are immense.'

However, the methods for estimating sulphur content in those days were rough and ready and the actual concentrations proved to be far below those stated. Areas on the island that had looked like beds of pure sulphur were shown to consist of iron pyrites, aptly called fool's gold. The higher-than-expected production costs of mining on the volcano and expensive delays in loading and transport because of the exposed situation of the island contributed to the burden.

Then there was the question of whether the fertiliser actually worked. Some farmers who undertook short trials with the product claimed good results, but others believed it was a scam. They said that far from helping growth, the fertiliser would actually burn grass off the paddocks. Still, there was a ready enough agricultural market.

Of course farmers were not the only beneficiaries. Many visitors to the island today recall how their mothers gave them sulphur and treacle as a tonic to ward off colds and flu. Others tell of sulphur being sprinkled in their fathers' socks at war to prevent fungal infections. Some remember how their mothers burnt sulphur to fumigate their houses. Bay of Plenty fishermen often went ashore to collect sulphur to rub into cuts that wouldn't heal. Sulphur-based medicines were among the first to be used to treat microbial and bacterial infection and are still in use today. Recently developed sulphur soap has proven helpful to those suffering from eczema and also acne.

Other common uses for sulphur today include the production of matches, the manufacture of gunpowder and the vulcanising of rubber. Sulphur is widely used as a preservative and also utilised in sterilising wine corks. Combined with lime it is effective as a fungicide on plants, and, when mixed with various fillers, sulphur forms a cement used to anchor metal objects to concrete.

But White Island's sulphur production days are over. Today nearly all of New Zealand's sulphur is imported and its predominant use is still in the fertiliser industry. Nearly 90% of the world's sulphur is converted to sulphuric acid, one of the most important industrial chemicals.

THERE IS PLANT LIFE ON WHITE ISLAND!

DESPITE THE HOSTILE ENVIRONMENT and acidic soil some vegetation does exist on White Island. The flora are not what one would consider healthy specimens — more survivors.

Within the main crater area at present there is no plant life, but in the creek bed and around some of the vents algae thrive. Microbacteria are also present in the lake water.

ABOVE: *The ice-plant is a native to New Zealand and it thrives on the ridges below the gannet colonies. Each day the bright little flowers turn to follow the path of the sun across the sky.*

As many as 13 different species of vegetation have been identified over the years on the outer walls of White Island, despite the acidic soil — rich in phosphates and low in nitrates. Add to this the acid rain and the occasional doses of volcanic ash from overhead and it is amazing anything can grow at all.

The most evident specimen is the pohutukawa tree (*Metrosideros excelsa*). The lower outer slopes of the volcano are covered in pohutukawa forest, with trees in varying states of health. Those on the southern side appear dead, although early photos indicate these were beautifully healthy until the eruption period that began in 1976. The forest has been estimated to be over 100 years old and it is hoped that, given enough eruption-free time, it may re-establish itself.

Curiously, these dead trees do not appear to be rotting; perhaps the acid climate is essentially preserving the timber. Ice-plant (*Disphyma australe*) grows profusely below the gannet colonies and looks like fleshy-bladed grass. Research shows that this plant, like sulphur, may contain anti-bacterial properties. The Maori used its juice to treat boils.

Although we have not been able to find all of the 13 species, the other plants we have identified are a native taupata (*Coprosma repens*), the water fern (*Histiopteris incisa*), native flax (*Phormium tenax*) and inkweed (*Phytolacca octandra*). None of these has been found in abundance.

Until White Island shows a significant decline in volcanic activity, plant life will be challenged, to say the least. Any significant reduction in the acidity of both the atmosphere and the soil would make for a more hospitable growing environment.

ABOVE: *Peter Tait stands among the stark remains of the pohutukawa forest on the northern side of White Island. Although the trees have died they don't appear to be rotting.*

ABOVE: *Long-spined diadema sea urchin display their brilliant armoury.*

INSET: *Several types of moray eel inhabit the waters around the island. As divers swim by, the eels come out of their hiding spots and follow the intruders' movements.*

FAR RIGHT: *Large schools of blue maomao can be viewed from the boat feeding on the surface, but an unforgettable experience awaits those who venture into the water.*

DIVERS' PARADISE

TO DIVE AT WHITE ISLAND is to enter an undersea world of spectacular beauty. Water temperatures reach a balmy 24°C in the summer and a 'low' of 14°C in the winter, and visibility at times exceeds 50 metres, making this truly a divers' paradise. Yet because of the distance from the mainland, White Island is not nearly as busy as some of the more popular dive sites around New Zealand.

There are a number of underwater vents emitting heated water. Surrounding these is usually a layer of white bacteria resembling a sheet of cotton wool. Diving in this is like being in a great spa bath.

One of the more common fish around White Island is the blue maomao.

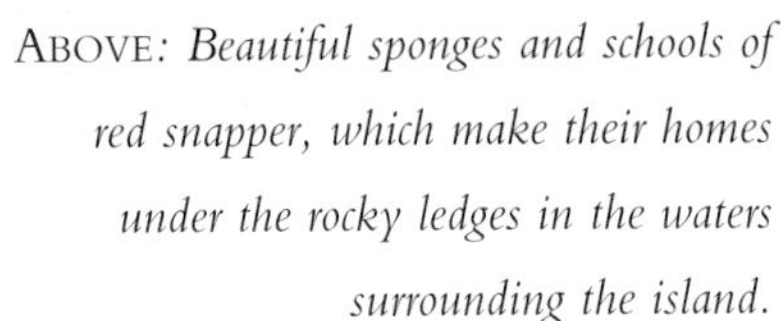

ABOVE: *Beautiful sponges and schools of red snapper, which make their homes under the rocky ledges in the waters surrounding the island.*

ABOVE RIGHT: *Scorpion fish, often called grandfather hapuka, are well suited to the rocky terrain surrounding the island. The fin spines can inflict painful stab wounds.*

As well as being abundant underwater they can be seen in huge schools on the surface — often up to 100 metres across — with large trevally leading the way in search of food.

Demoiselles and moray eels are also common, as are red snapper, pink maomao, blue moki, tarakihi, scorpion fish, leatherjackets, porae and a number of stingrays.

Under the surface a thick kelp forest hosts a variety of small plants and animals and the surrounding reefs are home to an abundance of sponges, lace-corals, starfish, sea squirts and other rock species. One of the more spectacular underwater sights is the long-spined iridescent diadema urchin, usually found in areas further north such as the Poor Knights Islands.

If you want more than scenery on your dive at White Island you may like to try for a packhorse crayfish. These giants inhabit the seabed and reefs in October and November, when they come into the shallows to lay their eggs.

Yellow-tail kingfish are abundant around the outlying reefs, and are also popular with sportsfishers and spearfishers.

To the west of White Island the Volkner Rocks also offer world-class diving. Up until 1998 these rocks were used for bombing practice by the New Zealand Air Force (not any more, we promise!). If you are lucky you may still find an old practice bomb lying on the seabed.

Diving at White Island in the past has meant spending a night on one of the overnight sportsfishing charter boats, but these days there are dedicated dive boats venturing to the island on a regular basis (weather permitting). A committee is at present working to form a marine reserve around the Volkner Rocks, to preserve this magical underworld for generations to come.

ABOVE: *Packhorse crayfish come into the shallow waters of the island for about six weeks at the end of each year. It takes only one of these to fill a dive bag.*

GANNETS AND MUTTONBIRDS

WHITE ISLAND is a successful breeding ground for the Australasian gannet and the grey-faced petrel.

About 5000 breeding pairs of gannets use the island each year, inhabiting the southern and western outer ridges. The soft surface and an abundance of seaweed around the island make this a perfect place to build their nests, and the surrounding waters provide a wonderful feeding ground.

ABOVE: *Grey-faced petrel.*

(G.A. Taylor, Department of Conservation)

Recordings over the last 10 years show that the gannets usually arrive in the first week of July and have all left by the end of the following February. On leaving their nests the chicks make their way across the Tasman Sea to spend up to five years feeding along the Australian coast. On reaching sexual maturity they return to New Zealand to breed in the colonies where they were born. The attractive adult gannet has a wingspan of up to two metres. Its body is crystal white with black wingtips, and the head has a stunning yellow cap.

Visitors to White Island are often treated to the spectacle of gannets feeding. To catch their prey they dive deep into the water — sometimes from a height of 30 metres and at speeds of up to 145 km per hour.

The grey-faced petrel (North Island muttonbird) also uses White Island as a breeding ground — in far greater numbers than the gannet. Estimates put the petrel population as high as 60,000.

This bird is rarely seen on the island, however, as it flies in at night in the winter months and leaves again before daylight. It nests in burrows predominantly on the northern wall of the crater.

The muttonbirds are remarkable; although they fly in after dark they somehow manage to crash through the shielding trees and head for their own burrow, finding it among the thousands on offer. Before dawn they climb the sloping trunks of trees to gain elevation to enable them to fly off.

A small number of gulls and terns also use White Island and the surrounding rocks for nesting.

ABOVE: *At sunset a handsome young gannet awaits dinner, courtesy of a returning parent.*

LEFT: *The majestic gannets with their fluffy chicks in a colony on a southern ridge of White Island. To build a nest the gannet forms a mound in the soft ash and lines it with seaweed. These nests are built within close proximity but just out of reach of other gannets.*

RIGHT: *The remains of the machinery are not only corroding away but also slowly being buried by erupted material.*

FAR RIGHT: *A bit of oil, perhaps? Corroding machinery within the remaining mining building.*

ABOVE: *The only retort left in the building.*

CORROSION PLUS

THERE'S NO ENVIRONMENT like it. Some days it is steamy and mystical like a scene from a horror movie; at other times the place looks as if it is on fire. Always it is strangely, hauntingly beautiful.

Scientists tell us that White Island has been 'degassing' for at least 16,000 years. It discharges gases at temperatures ranging from 100°C to 800°C — mostly steam, carbon dioxide and sulphur dioxide, with small amounts of halogen gases.

The approximate proportions of the gas by weight are 75% water, 18% carbon dioxide and 5% sulphur dioxide, giving an average daily volume of about 2600 tons of carbon dioxide and 400 tons of sulphur dioxide. Needless to say, this is less than helpful for the problem of greenhouse gas emissions.

In fine weather it is not a problem for visitors to the island, but on

RIGHT: *What happened to my shirt? Sulphur dioxide in the atmosphere acts as a bleach. (The darker patches were protected from the steam by this person's bag.)*

BELOW: *Fordson tractor, 1978. Notice how the rubber on the wheels withstands the conditions, while the metal does not.* (A. Moore)

FAR RIGHT: *A moody place: strangely, hauntingly beautiful.*

INSET FAR RIGHT: *Steam condensing on cold clothing gives some unusual effects.* (B.Todd)

overcast days or with the wrong wind direction they must wear gas masks with acid filters, and are also advised to cover cameras, jewellery and other metal objects. The acid gases combine with water in the steam to form liquid acid droplets that not only sting your eyes and skin but corrode metal as well.

The sulphur dioxide in the steam acts as a bleach, which reacts with some fibres and dyes so it is not uncommon for clothing to change colour. Fortunately this is temporary — these garments will return to their original colour when washed.

On cold days the steam can be seen to condense on clothing so that wherever people walk they leave a steam trail!

The effect of the corrosive atmosphere is clearly visible on the metal of the machinery left when mining ceased. It can also be seen in the walls of

the remaining building, where the reinforcing steel of the concrete is corroding, swelling and bursting the concrete as if it has some form of concrete cancer. The timber, meanwhile, is beautifully preserved, as is the rubber on the wheels of the old tractor.

The acidic atmosphere is hard on the White Island Tours vessel too: the stainless steel tends to go black and the white paint turns orange. A strict daily cleaning regime preserves the appearance of the craft, and ensures that it is maintained in safe working order.

But there is no record that the fumes adversely affected the health of the miners; in fact some thought the atmosphere beneficial. Gatland Gilberd, an engineer on the island from 1927–30, claimed to have been cured of asthma during those years.

Perhaps the island has a future as a health farm!

THE FUTURE

WITH ITS MINING DAYS OVER and its status as a scenic reserve, what does the future hold for White Island?

The island's unique habitat means scientists are likely to retain their strong interest and presence. The volcano is of continuing scientific importance and interest to volcanologists, particularly with its crater being so accessible. The acidic environment and the sparse plant growth make it a fascinating place for botanists.

While microalgae studies have been limited, the acidic lake may well eventually yield some interesting stories. The uniqueness of the island's underwater environment will only be enhanced if the proposed marine reserve goes ahead.

White Island has already been used as a natural laboratory for studying the reactions of metals under severe conditions and could be the site of tests on other materials. It would be a perfect spot for a study of the effects of erosion on the earth's surface.

Some visitors think White Island should become a health resort, with its thermal water and sulphur deposits; others believe it would be a good site for a prison farm, with its remoteness and hostile environment. Neither venture is likely in the near future!

But what of the future of tourism on White Island? While it is a fascinating place for tourists to visit, an explosion in tourist numbers would be harmful to the natural environment. In this respect the island's hostile habitat is probably its salvation. The island is 49 km offshore in exposed conditions, there are no sophisticated landing areas, and only two bays are accessible by boat. These face south and south-east, making it impossible to land in strong winds.

From our years of running tours to White Island we have come to recognise that these limiting factors are essential to the conservation of this unique place.